MW00613548

www.DiscoverLSP.com   PRODUCTS & PUBLISHING

Copyright © 2017
Life Science Publishing, Pamela Hunter, & Stacey Vann
1.800.336.6308
www.DiscoverLSP.com

Printed in the United States of America
10 9 8 7 6 5 4 3 2 1

"*Breath is the bridge which connects life to consciousness, which unites your body to your thoughts. Whenever your mind becomes scattered, use your breath as the means to take hold of your mind again.*"
— Thich Nhít Hính

"*Master the breath, let the self be in bliss, contemplate on the sublime within you.*"
— Tirumalai Krishnamacharya

"*When you own your breath, nobody can steal your peace.*"
— Author Unknown

"Like water which can clearly mirror the sky and the trees only so long as its surface is undisturbed, the mind can only reflect the true image of the Self when it is tranquil and wholly relaxed."
— Indra Devi

FOREWORD

Whether this is your first step in living a cleaner, greener, more health-conscious life, or you're a long-time devotee of green living, essential oils are a godsend. They have the power to change people's lives. I happen to know firsthand!

At the age of 21, I was told that I would not live to see 30 because of a serious autoimmune disease. My only chance at survival? Over 15 months of grueling, heartbreaking chemotherapy. It was a long-hard battle—one that I still face every day. And, I couldn't do it without my Young Living Essential Oils.

I'm a long way past 30 (or maybe I've just turned 29 a few times), but I have to say this new lease on life inspired me to make a difference. The past two decades I've devoted myself to the cause of education. But I'm not talking about the make-you-snore-take-a-test-and-forget kind of learning. (Obviously, that has its place. I think…) I'm talking about real knowledge that people can use right away. I'm talking about the self-empowering kind of education, the kind that really frees you to take your life, your health, and your future into your own hands.

In fact, this volume and its many companion volumes are the perfect way to get not only acquainted with essential oils and their many uses, but to do something with them right away. Today, in fact. Every year, my team and I search for the best, most updated information and scientific studies to continue building practical education tools for people to use. It has become an ongoing labor of love and a personal passion. I firmly believe that education is the key to improving the health and lives of everyone in this world. I'm particularly proud of the work Pamela and Stacey have done to share with you the important information in this volume about a fuller mind-body connection.

My company, Life Science Publishing, has been around since Young Living's beginning. While I wasn't there when the doors opened, I certainly know the daily struggles that come with being an entrepreneur. There are constant ups and downs. I can't say they are easy, but I would say they are worth it. I have turned to great mentors in my life, and I believe we can all learn from someone who has been in our shoes before.

Now, I'm not here to sell you oils. I'm here to invite you to learn the simple, practical ways they can make a difference in your life—and the lives of the loved ones around you. I'm here to help you get introduced to oils and help you learn how to put them into your own homemade recipes and solutions. The steps that Pamela & Stacey provide help you to take immediate action—to put yoga techniques into practice right away.

I would love to say we've met, but if all you know of me is the picture in this book, I hope to meet you soon! I've been told that my energy and passion are contagious. If that's the case, I hope you catch them both…

Love. Learn. Share.

xoxo

Troie Battles

Troie Storms-Battles

ABOUT THE AUTHORS

Pamela Hunter and Stacey Vann have been teaching yoga together since 1999 and experiencing Young Living Essential Oils since 2002. Pamela & Stacey are members of the faculty for Young Living Essential Oils: Balance Yoga and Wellness Retreats offered around the globe.

Founder of Fun Lovin' Wellness, Pamela Hunter believes in awakening awareness and opening paths. Pamela's journey has inspired her and many others to learn and share self-care practices. Pamela creates community through her love and education as a leader for Young Living Essential Oils sharing "little bottles of love." She has taught yoga since 2001 and is E-RYT 500, CYKT, a Certified UZIT (Urban Zen Integrative Therapy) and Internationally respected Integrative Health Coach. She is also certified in several mindful modalities: Clinical Aromatherapy, Spiritual Healing, Reiki, and Reflexology. She is the author of Rise & Shine: 6 Master Steps to Get Moving. She resides in Chicago area with her husband. Her two grown sons are in college. Pamela is traveling, teaching retreats and workshops, writing, and still growing!

www.FunLovinWellness.com

"We transform our body and our mind to meet our soul."
— Pamela Hunter

ABOUT THE AUTHORS

Stacey Vann, E-RYT 500 began teaching yoga in 1997 and started her journey with Young Living in 2002. She weaves and shares the transformative and integrative path of yoga, sound, and Young Living essential oils in the United States and internationally. Stacey's teaching style is infused with laughter, energy, and love. She encourages her students to attain wellness, joy, and connection with a commitment to daily practice, self-care, and an attitude of gratitude.

Stacey Vann is a mother, Life Coach, doula, reflexologist, Young Living essential oil educator and founder of the Mahabhuta Yoga Festival, co-founder of Galactic Child Yoga, and is co-owner of Breathe Yoga and Wellness Center where she leads 200 & 300-hour teacher training programs in Pensacola, Florida.

www.StaceyVann.com

"Breathe Deeply, Move Freely, & Live Joyfully."
— Stacey Vann

TABLE OF CONTENTS

THE STORY OF TORTOISE AND DOG

We would like to tell you the story about Tortoise and her good friend, Dog. Tortoise and Dog were born on the same day on a farm. They soon became fast friends. Tortoise moved a lot slower than her friend, Dog. She always wished she could run and keep up with how fast Dog could move around the farm. Dog was all over the place – running, nipping, jumping, rolling, scratching, panting – going wherever her mind would take her. Tortoise took care of her important daily duties with time for play, rest, and self-care.

Every day they would meet at the creek to play in the water. They spent many afternoons there. Many years passed and Tortoise began to notice that her friend, Dog, was starting to move much slower than usual. Tortoise was able to move at a steady pace, the way she has always moved. One day, Dog's daughter, Puppy, showed up at the creek without her

mom. She shared with Tortoise that her mom had gone to the Rainbow Bridge. Puppy soon became Tortoise's best friend. Tortoise noticed that Puppy ran fast around the farm just like her mother. Many years passed and Puppy became just like her mom – much slower. And one day at the river, Granddaughter Puppy showed up at the creek to let Tortoise know that her mom, Puppy had crossed the Rainbow Bridge. Tortoise met SEVEN generations from her best friend, Dog.

Tortoise still moved at the same steady pace and lived to be over 100 years old, while all her Doggie best friends only lived 15 years each. Tortoise wondered why?

Great Owl came to visit and explained why Tortoise lived so much longer than Dog and all the Puppies.

Great Owl asked, *"Have you ever noticed how dogs breathe?"*

"Why yes! Dog and all the generations of Puppies panted and breathed very quickly – like FAST! I always thought they were out of breath." replied Tortoise.

Great Owl asked Tortoise, *"How do you breathe?"*

"I breathe slowly, deeply, and evenly. I breathe about 1 breath per minute," Tortoise realized. *"How many breaths per minute do all my doggie friends breathe?"*

Great Owl shared, *"Dogs breathe 10 - 35 breaths per minute. They rest at 25 breaths per minute. You are given a certain amount of breaths in each lifetime. Use them wisely."*

Tortoise appreciates her friends that move fast, but more so, appreciates her steady pace and steady breath.

ARE YOU LIKE TORTOISE OR DOG?

The average healthy adult breathes 12 – 20 breaths per minute. Our body automatically breathes in and out. We take our breath for granted. How long can you live without air? Not long, air is vital to our life energy. It takes practice to become conscious of our breath. A steady breath reflects a steady mind. Notice how you breathe when you are running all around, feeling anxious, agitated, and stressed. Are you like Dog?

Humans have the capacity to slow the breath and be mindful of this air moving in and out, steadily, deeply, and evenly. In this book, we share breathing practices as self-care tools to become more mindful breathers. Our motivation is for all of us to connect to our life energy, practice self-care, and to breathe more like Tortoise.

WHAT IS BREATHING?

Breathing is the cycle of moving air in and out of the lungs. The lungs bring oxygen to the body's cells with the inhalation and release the carbon dioxide with the exhalation. We inhale life energy and we exhale toxins, waste, and stagnant energy. The diaphragm muscle is the vitality center of our body. When you breathe in (inhale), the brain sends a message to the diaphragm to contract (lower and flatten) bringing in air. Once the air is in, as you breath out (exhale), the diaphragm relaxes (rise and expand) into its dome shape under the ribs. The average adult breathes between 12 – 20 breaths per minute.

WHAT IS MINDFUL BREATHING?

Your breath is your life energy. Mindful Breathing is the practice to increase and extend your life energy. We learn to regulate our breath to 4 - 8 breaths per minute increasing our lung capacity.

Increase lung capacity = Increase life energy

Mindful Breathing allows us to feel and become more aware of the connection between our minds and our bodies. Our life force increases as we learn to expand and contract our breath. Everyone breathes to live, however, they may not mindful of their breathing. It is potent to know how to breathe.

Mindful Breathing is versatile—from simple to complex. There are so many practices in which to experience the life energy within you. We look forward to practicing with you!

WHY PRACTICE MINDFUL BREATHING?

Practicing may help us:
- Learn the proper way to breathe
- Bring more oxygen to the body
- Support reduced toxicity in the body
- Support healthy waste elimination
- Develop concentration and focus
- Relax the body and the mind
- Bring us peace of mind
- Be in equanimity within our own self and our environment
- Support emotional balance
- Support all the systems of the body

WHAT ARE ESSENTIAL OILS?

Essential Oils are volatile liquids distilled from roots, stems, leaves, flowers, bark or resin of plants. They are the life energy of the plant kingdom. This life energy extends the wellness and life of the plant.

Essential Oils are potent, highly complex and concentrated substances containing anywhere from 80 – 300 chemical compounds serving the plant for optimum wellness.

Essential Oils are versatile. Essential oil can be used for a variety of needs to support you and keep you above the wellness line (the wellness line is an imaginary line we draw between health issues and optimum wellness).

Essential Oils are also versatile in their application and can be used in the following ways:

Inhalation

Simply breathing in essential oils is amazing! The sense of smell is the only sense that travels directly to the brain. The essential oil aroma travels through the olfactory bulb to the Limbic brain where memory and emotions are stored.

Diffusing, Scent Tent, Cotton Pad, and Direct from the Bottle are ways we will use the inhalation method during our Breathing Practices.

Topical

The intelligence of essential oils is fascinating! Applying neat or diluted, directly to a location may enhance the physical, mental, emotional, and spiritual awareness in the body.

The bottom of the feet is said to be the safest place to apply topically. The essential oils have their own intelligence and travel where they are needed in the body.

There are various topical applications we will be demonstrating for our Breathing Practices.

Internally

Overall wellness support is brilliant! Young Living Essential Oils has an entire line of Vitality Essential Oils to be used as dietary supplements. Vitality Oils support the systems of the body for overall wellness. When using the topical application for our Breathing Practices, if there is Vitality Oil that matches the topical oils you are using, it is also supportive to our body systems.

WHY PRACTICE MINDFUL BREATHING WITH ESSENTIAL OILS

Essential Oils are a simple, safe, and effective addition to the practice and when added to Mindful Breathing they magnify the benefits listed earlier. Putting essential oils and Mindful Breathing together creates a synergy for a lifestyle of wellness. When you work with these practices, you will feel the life energy of your breath and the essential oils!

Every one of us already has the seeds of mindfulness.
The practice is to cultivate it.
— Thích Nhít Hính

BASIC GUIDELINES FOR SAFE USE

STORAGE	CAUTIONARY USE	Application
Store in amber bottles	Oils rich in menthol (peppermint) are not suggested to be used on neck or throat area of children < 18 months	Topically apply oils to bottoms of feet or use in bath water, no more than 10 drops
Capped tightly	Citrus oils, Bergamot are photosensitive. Stay out of sun, 1-2 days after application or cover usage area.	Direct inhalation of oils, up to 10-15 times daily
Keep in cool location, out of light	Keep essential oils from eyes and ears. Do not touch eyes, glasses, or contact lenses.	Inhalation of oils not recommended for asthmatics
Keep out of reach of children	People exhibiting chronic, pre-existing health conditions (epilepsy, hypertension, i.e.) should consult physician before use. Particular caution with high ketone oils such as, Basil, Rosemary, Sage, and Tansy oils.	Before internal ingestion, try dilution in Blue Agave, Yacon syrups, or olive or coconut oils, rice milk
Keep vegetable oil on hand for dilution (V-6 Oil complex, other veggie oils)	Pregnant women or people exhibiting allergies should consult their physicians prior to use. Dilution of oils with a vegetable-based oil suggested. Skin patch test on the underside of the arm for 30 minutes warranted. Use common sense.	Reactions to essential oils, topically or by ingestion, may be delayed 2-3 days after use

Chemical Sensitivities & Allergies: Those with extra-sensitive skin, who begin using ultra-pure essential oils, will experience rashes or reactions. This may occur with an undiluted spice, conifer, or the citrus oils. An oil may react with petroleum-based residues which remain in fatty tissue from personal care products that have leached into the skin.

Before beginning with oils, try a skin test. Spot test on an area such as the inside of the forearm at the elbow. Apply one oil or blend at one time. If layering a new oil, allow 3-5 minutes to assess for a reaction, before testing a different oil. If you express a sensitivity, then follow the dilution protocol.

DILUTE:
- Dilute 1-3 drops of essential oil in ½ teaspoon of Young Living's V-6 Vegetable Oil Complex, massage oil, or any pure vegetable oil such as almond, coconut, avocado, or olive. More dilution may be required.
- Reduce the number of oils used at any time.
- Use single oils or oil blends one at a time.
- Reduce the amount of oil used.
- Reduce the frequency of application.
- Drink more purified or distilled water.
- **UTILIZE NATURAL HOUSEHOLD CLEANING SOLUTIONS TO REDUCE DAILY CHEMICAL EXPOSURES**

Asthmatic Caution:
When using essential oils for breathing practices, please apply your oils as far away from the lungs as possible. Use caution with Lavender.

Contraidications for Mindful Breathing Practices with Essential Oils:
- Do not practice while experiencing fever, flu, pneumonia, bronchitis, or breathing difficulties.
- Do not practice if you have a recent history of heart attack.
- Do not practice if you are undergoing chemo or radiation therapy or highly metastasized cancer.
- Do not practice if you have severe psychological conditions.
- Consult your physicians if you have high blood pressure, heart problems, migraine headaches, vertigo, or epilepsy before practicing.
- Consult your physician if you are pregnant or having a heavy menstrual cycle.

Guidelines for Practicing:

- Wear comfortable, loose clothing.
- Practice on an empty or light stomach.
- When seated, the knees are below the hips. The spine is straight with the chin floating over the collarbone. The throat is relaxed. The eyes are soft. The heart is lifted.
- Quiet, serene spaces without distractions are preferred, but not required.
- Put your cell phone on "Do Not Disturb."
- Supplies you may desire for maximum support: chair, blanket, bolster, meditation cushion, and/or a shawl.
- Have your Young Living Essential Oils close by and pick your own or choose from our favorites listed after each practice.
- Age range recommended for at least 12 years of age.

FEELING THE BREATH

All you need is your breath and your desired essential oil. Feeling the Breath can be done anywhere at anytime for any length of time desired.

Stop what you are doing and *notice* how you are breathing. Observe. How are you feeling right now?

Bring your attention to your breath. No need to change or manipulate your breath, only observe.

Notice how it feels in your body. Is the breath cool or warm? Is the breath long or short? Is the mind calm, or is there a stream of thoughts?

Notice. As the breath leaves the body, notice each part of this experience. When the breath is long, notice that the breath is long. When the breath is short, notice that the breath is short. At any time, add in your essential oil using the inhalation method. How does the essential oil deepen your connection to your breath?

If (and when) there are thoughts that glide into your mind, allow the thoughts. Acknowledge them, release them, "tell them you will talk to them later" and then gently turn your attention back to the physical sensations of the breath. This is a process. Be with it, allow it, and release the thoughts without judgment as you return to your breath. It's fun, play with it.

You are toning your meditation muscles. Sometimes thoughts will drift for a while before you recognize it. That's ok. Gently bring it back. You are becoming one with your breath. You are feeling your breath and overcoming the obstacles of mind chatter and placing yourself back on track. Over time your mind will thank you. It will become calmer and the experience of Feeling the Breath will bring enhanced wellness.

Add essential oils to this practice easily and simply by:
1. Diffusing
2. Dripping 3 drops of an oil on a cotton pad to inhale when desired
3. Apply 1-3 drops in the palm of your hand, rub your hands together 3x clockwise. Bring your hands to your nose in a Scent Tent and inhale when desired.

Our Favorite Young Living Essential Oils for **Feeling the Breath**:
Pick one and connect with it.

- Breathe Again™
- Frankincense
- Juniper
- Myrtle
- Orange
- Present Time™
- Reconnect™
- Surrender™

- Eucalyptus Globulus
- Grounding™
- Lemon
- Northern Lights Black Spruce
- Pine
- Raven™
- Release™

"Wellness within is mindfulness and acceptance of what you are, what you feel inside and how it's always changing. That process is helped by being attentive to the breath as it moves through the body."
— **Rodney Yee**

COUNTING THE BREATH

Counting the breath is simply another way to settle the mind and to place attention with the breath. The act of counting can help hold the mind. Counting also makes it more noticeable when your mind has drifted into thought. This can be used as a calming introduction to a longer meditation period. Now is the time to apply your Young Living Essential Oil. We recommend using the topical method to the bottom of your feet for Counting the Breath.

Our favorite Young Living Essential Oils for **Counting the Breath**:
- Basil
- Clarity™
- Lemon
- Peppermint
- Sacred Frankincense™
- Vetiver
- Cedarwood
- Jade Lemon™
- Oola®*Balance™
- Reconnect™
- Valor®
- 3 Wise Men™

First, get comfortable. Let your body become settled and relaxed.

Begin to count each breath, inhale 1 - exhale 1, Inhale 2 - exhale 2... up to 10 and then start over. Keep your attention on counting and feeling the sensations of the breath. When you get distracted and the mind drifts, start again at 1. This practice may increase your awareness and enhance your focus. It may be helpful to initially make the counting more complex in order to hold your attention. In that case, you can go from 1 up to 10 and then backwards from 10 to 1.

Eventually with practice, the mind will require less complexity to focus. Then you may want to count once for a breath cycle (I inhale/exhale, 2 inhale/exhale...). Eventually, no counting will be necessary to hold your focus and you can be with your breath.

*Oola is a registered trademark of OolaMoola, LLC

LENGTHENING THE BREATH

Lengthening the breath is another practice to deepen your connection to feeling the breath. Counting 1-2-3-4 as you slowly inhale, pause 4 counts, exhale 1-2-3-4, and pause for 4 counts. When having a consistent and even - inhale, pause, exhale, pause - Once your breath becomes consistent with this practice of inhale, pause, exhale, pause, you may begin increasing the counting number to further lengthen the breath.

Giving attention to your breathing can be a wonderful tool!
Practice being aware.

Equaling your inhale and exhale, the breath is balancing.
Lengthening and holding your exhalation pause is relaxing.
Lengthening and holding your inhalation pause is energizing.

When feeling stressed, it is better to balance your breath with equal inhalation and exhalation.

Our Favorite Young Living Essential Oils for **Lengthening the Breath**:

Balancing
- Acceptance™
- Frankincense
- Idaho Balsam Fir
- Palo Santo
- Valor®
- Envision™
- Harmony™
- Oola®*Balance™
- Ylang Ylang
- White Angelica™

Relaxing
- Bergamot
- Gentle Baby™
- Jasmine
- Peace & Calming™
- Rose
- Stress Away™
- Clary Sage
- Geranium
- Lavender
- Roman Chamomile
- Sandalwood

Energizing
- Awaken
- Fulfill Your Destiny™
- Lemon
- Oola®*Fitness™
- Orange
- Tangerine
- En-R-Gee
- Highest Potential™
- Motivation™
- Oola®*Fun™
- Peppermint

*Oola is a registered trademark of OolaMoola, LLC

BELLY BREATHING (ABDOMINAL BREATH)

From a seated or supine (laying down) position, start by exhaling out through the nose and bringing your abdomen gently back towards the spine releasing all of your air. On the inhalation, as you breathe in through your nose, relax the abdomen, it will naturally rise and fill like a big balloon.

When you exhale again, your belly will deflate. It may help to place your palms or a beanie baby on the abdomen in order to feel the movements of the breath. Continue breathing until you have established a natural rhythm – inhale, the belly rises and fills up like a big balloon and exhale the belly falls and deflates the balloon. If the breathing muscles are tight, it can be helpful to practice this breath in a supine position with a bolster under the knees to relax.

In order to breathe deeply and expand your lung capacity, let's review the science of the breath. Ideally, the diaphragm contracts downward, and the belly will expand with oxygen. To expel the carbon dioxide, the diaphragm relaxes upward, compressing the lungs and expelling the air out; this causes the belly to sink. The abdominal region is very tight when you are under stress. *The abdomen is a nice place to apply 1-3 drops of your Young Living Essential Oils during Belly Breathing.*

Our Favorite Young Living Essential Oils for **Belly Breathing**:

- AromaEase™
- Fennel
- Gathering™
- Harmony™
- InnerChild™
- Purification®
- DiGize™
- Forgiveness™
- Ginger
- Humility™
- Oola®*Family™
- Transformation™

Oola is a registered trademark of OolaMoola, LLC

THREE-PART BREATHING
(COMPLETE YOGIC BREATH)

Three-Part Inhale:
1. Inhale, concentrate on filling the lower lungs.
   Feel the abdomen expand.
2. Continue to inhale, filling the middle lungs.
   Feel the rib cage expand.
3. Inhale all the way into the upper lungs.
   Feel the collarbones expand.

Three-Part Exhale:
1. Exhale. First deflate the upper lungs.
2. Continue exhaling and deflating the middle lungs.
3. Exhale fully, feeling the abdomen contract,
   expelling the rest of your air.

Continue this practice, allowing the breath to become steady and rhythmic, like a wave.

Bring in your Young Living Essential Oils dropping 1-3 drops in the palm of your hand, rubbing your hands together 3x and using the Scent Tent as you inhale. Prayer to Heart as you exhale.

Our Favorite Young Living Essential Oils for **Three-Part Breathing with Scent Tent and Prayer to Heart**:
- Abundance™
- Joy™
- Sacred Frankincense
- Sacred Sandalwood
- White Angelica™
- Inspiration™
- Rose
- Sacred Mountain™
- The Gift™

THREE-PART BREATHING
(LIGHT & LOVE BREATH)

Light & Love Breath is another way to practice **Three-Part Breathing**. By placing one hand on your heart and one hand on your solar plexus (just above the navel) we connect with our powerful LIGHT, balancing it with our powerful LOVE!

Your essential oil technique here can be a combo of two oils - one on your navel and one on your heart.

Our Favorite Young Living Essential Oils combos for **Light & Love Breath**:
- Forgiveness™ on the navel and Frankincense on your heart.
- Harmony™ on the navel and Joy on your heart.
- Ylang Ylang on the navel and AromaLife™ on your heart
- Neroli on the navel and Rose on the heart
- Pick your favorite pair!

SCENT TENT

PRAYER TO HEART

"As you breathe in, cherish yourself. As you breathe out, cherish all Beings."
— Dalai Lama XIV

BALANCING BREATH
(ALTERNATIVE NOSTRIL BREATHING)

Balancing Breath is a calming breathing technique, where you alternate inhaling and exhaling between each nostril.

By practicing a few rounds of Balancing Breath each day, you may:
- Balance the right and left hemispheres of your brain
- Support a restful night sleep
- Calm your emotions and the mind
- Support a healthy nervous system

The amount of airflow naturally alternates from one nostril to the next approximately every 2-3 hours. Right now, we are favoring either the left or the right nostril and are generally unaware of this naturally occurring process.

Breathing through the right nostril affects the left thinking/logical side of the brain. Breathing through the left nostril affects the feeling/emotional side of the brain. When we alternate breathing between the two nostrils, we bring balance to both sides.

To bring your Young Living Essential Oils into this practice, it is fun to dip your ring finger and thumb into an essential oil before beginning this practice.

Our Favorite Young Living Essential Oils for the **Balancing Breath**:
- AromaLife™
- Eucalyptus *globulus*
- R.C.™
- Sacred Sandalwood
- 3 Wise Men™
- Dorato Azul™
- Eucalyptus *radiata*
- Sacred Frankincense
- Tea Tree (*Melaleuca alternafolia*)

BALANCING BREATH PRACTICE

1) First, get settled and comfortable in a seated position, spine straight.
2) Place the left hand in the lap, palm up, bringing the thumb and pointer finger together.
3) Take your right hand, fold your pointer and middle fingers into your palm resting on the padded part of your thumb. This allows your thumb, ring, and pinky finger to be up. This is the life energy hand gesture, mudra.

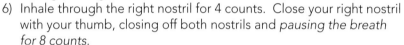

4) Close your nostril with your right thumb and breathe out, gently and slowly through the left nostril, and then inhale a 4-count breath through the left nostril to begin.
5) Close your left nostril with your ring finger, closing off both nostrils and pausing the breath for 8 counts. Lift your thumb and exhale through the right nostril for 4 counts.
6) Inhale through the right nostril for 4 counts. Close your right nostril with your thumb, closing off both nostrils and *pausing the breath for 8 counts.*
7) Lift your ring finger and exhale through the left nostril for 4 counts. This completes one full cycle of Balance Breathing. You always begin and end on your left nostril.
8) Continue for 8 rounds, beginning always on the left nostril. This practice gives power, strength, and vitality. It can have a cooling, cleansing effect. Initially, the tongue tastes bitter, and will eventually become sweet.

It is nice to practice Balancing Breath at sunrise and/or sunset.

COOLING BREATH

1. Sit in a comfortable seated position.
2. Breath in by rolling the tongue into a "U," with the tip just outside of the lips. If you cannot shape the tongue into a "U" (you were born with this muscle in the tongue or not – don't sweat it), extend the tongue past the lips with the mouth slightly open.
3. Inhale deeply through the rolled tongue, exhale through the nose. Can you feel the coolness of the breath on your tongue as you inhale?
4. Continue for 3 minutes.

Practicing this Cooling Breath is a deep meditation and supports a healthy digestive system. To add your Young Living Essential Oils to this practice, place a toothpick amount or up to 1 drop of Vitality Essential Oils to the tip of your tongue.

Our Favorite Young Living Essential Oils for **Cooling Breath**:
- Digize Vitality™
- Endoflex Vitality™
- Peppermint Vitality™
- Spearmint Vitality™

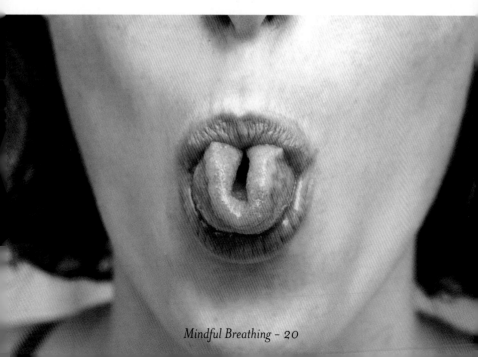

HEART-CENTERED BREATHING

After dropping your Young Living Essential Oils in your palms, place your hands at your heart in prayer position or layer your hands on your heart.

Breathe into your belly as you open your arms out to the sides, expanding your chest and arms. Your arms form a letter T moving with your inhale. Pause as you are open and extend.

As you exhale, bring the arms back into your chest with your hands at your heart, moving as you exhale slowly and with mindfulness. When your hands are at your heart again, pause, holding your breath for a brief moment.

Then you inhale, begin again, continuing this movement for 3 – 6 more times. You are brushing your heart-centered field with openness, love, and protection.

Our Favorite Young Living Essential Oils for **Heart-Centered Breathing**:
- Frankincense
- Joy™
- Rose
- Sensation™
- Geranium
- Orange
- Sacred Frankincense

"Breathing is meditation; life is a meditation. You have to breathe in order to live, so breathing is how you get in touch with the sacred space of your heart."
— Willow Smith

BREATHING FOR KIDS

By tuning into the breath before the practice of yoga, we encourage children to listen to their bodies and tune into how they feel. The goal is to recognize the connection between the body, breath, and spirit in subtle ways. For younger children, the breathing techniques can be explored using fun games or teaching tools. We can teach older children deeper lessons about the their emotions and show them how we can use the breath to transform these feelings. Overall, teaching children how to breathe properly, is an amazing tool.

Look for one of our books on Breathing for Kids in the future.

Mindful B

Thank you for practicing Mindful Breathing with Essential Oils!

An attitude of gratitude is the highest form of prayer. Use these affirmations to express your gratitude:

Expression	*Affirmation*
Be grateful for your breath.	I am grateful for my breath.
Be grateful for your body.	I am grateful for your body.
Be grateful for your essential oils.	I am grateful for my essential oils.
Be grateful for all of your experiences.	I am grateful for all my experiences.

Know that you are beautiful, bountiful, and blissful.

As humans, we have the choice to live like the Tortoise or the Dog. Whatever you choose, take in the sweetness of life and be grateful.

We are grateful for your presence, participation, and support for our *Mindful Breathing with Essential Oils* book!

"Life is not an emergency,
but a celebration of every breath we are
given in this lifetime."
— Stacey Vann

LEARN MORE...

This is just a whiff of Mindful Breathing with Essential Oils. The oils mentioned are only a fraction of the collection. Talk to your local Young Living member about all of the collection as well as discounts and rewards for using Young Living products.

Join us for a Young Living Balance, Yoga, & Wellness Retreat to get firsthand practice and education about yoga and essential oils. www.youngliving.com/events

Look for more of our books coming to Life Science Publishers.

Mindful B   - 24